SEE THE STABLE

Words and music by Alison Hedger

A celebration of the Christmas Story in music

for children up to 12 years.
Approximate length 25 – 30 minutes

Biblical texts are given.
Suitable for schools and Sunday schools.

Piano accompaniment, with vocal lines and guitar chords for 8 new carols. Ideas for recorders and pitched and non-pitched percussion: some simple 2 part singing.

1. **The Angel Gabriel**
   Optional second part verse 4.
   Solo Gabriel. Chimes and Drum.

2. **Bethlehem Travellers**
   Solo Mary and Joseph (and duet). Metallophone.

3. **The Inn Is Full**
   Recorders, Snare Drum, Indian Bells, and Glockenspiel.

4. **Go To Bethlehem**

5. **Fascinated By That Star**
   Recorders – Woodblock – Cymbals.

6. **Who's That Knocking?**
   Optional short solos for Joseph, Shepherds, Kings etc.
   Woodblock.

7. **See The Stable**
   Recorder.

8. **Christmas Bells**
   Bells, Tambourine, Drums and Cymbals.
   Audience clapping.

© Copyright 1987 Golden Apple Productions
A division of Chester Music Limited
8/9 Frith Street, London W1V 5TZ

GA 10259
ISBN 1 870997 06 9

A cassette of the music in this book is also available
Order No. GA 10267

5.95

1.
The Angel Gabriel

Luke 1 v.26–38

3

4

While myr - iad an - gels sing, 'Good will to men and Peace on Earth, All Praise to God our King.'

CHIMES for verse 4

Drum

5.
Fascinated By That Star

N.B. Cymbals ✳ should be 'sliced'

Matthew 2 v.1–12

1. Three Wise Men came from a - far, Fol-low-ing a bright new star. Came from miles and miles to see, What this strange new light might be.

2. Cas-par, Mel-chi-or and Bal-tha-zar, Fas-ci-na-ted by that star,

16

Sym - bo - li - zing what would be – This was Christ's Na - ti - vi - ty.

8ve higher

glissando

Bass in 8ves to end

The vocal line with the part 2 on the glockenspiel is an alternative idea.

Recorder 1

Recorder 2

6.
Who's That Knocking?

It may be preferred to have everyone sing all the song as it will prove very popular with the youngest of singers.

Who's that knock-ing at the sta - ble door? Ask-ing if they may come in?
We all knocked at the sta - ble door, Ask-ing if we might come in.

WOODBLOCK OR CLAPPING

Who's that knock-ing at the sta - ble door? Jo-seph, shall we let them in?
We all knocked at the sta - ble door, Jo-seph kind-ly let us in.

FINE

1. 'The keep - ers of the inn.'
2. 'The tra - vellers from a - far.'
'Who goes there?' 3. 'The shep - herds from the hill.'   'Shall I let them in?'   'Yes   please.'
4. 'The three___ wise___ men.'
5. 'The child - ren of the world.'

JOSEPH   CHARACTERS   JOSEPH   MARY

Who's that knock - ing at the sta - ble door,   Ask - ing if they may come   in?
ALL

*Play the introduction
between each verse*

Relaxation

The underlying secret of good drumming is in the complete relaxation of fingers, hands, wrists, and arms. Unless you can learn to relax these muscles your drumming will never be smooth and rhythmical.

Holding the Sticks

The Right Hand

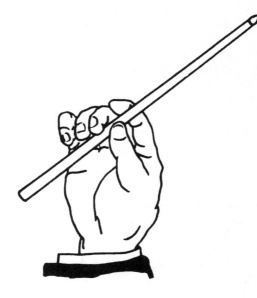

(3)

The Hold

The drum stick is held in the right hand by the fleshy part of the thumb and the first (1st) joint of the first finger. (SEE SKETCH 3) This is the pivoting point. The balancing point will have to be determined by the individual according to the type of stick used, generally about $\frac{2}{3}$ of the stick down and $\frac{1}{3}$ up. Palm of right hand is down. (SEE SKETCH 4) The action of this stick is controlled by the 2nd finger.

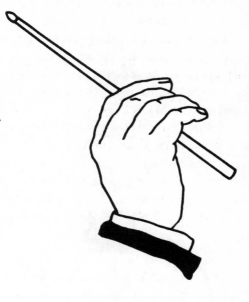

(4)

Playing Position

The Left Hand

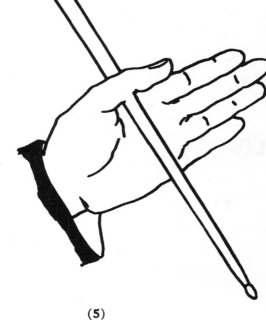

(5)

The Hold

The drum stick is held in the left hand by the crotch between the thumb and 1st finger. (SEE SKETCH 5) This is the pivoting point. The third and fourth fingers are curled under the stick with the second joint of the third finger acting as the balancing point. This third finger also serves to lift the stick after each stroke. The 1st and 2nd fingers are curled above or on top of the stick. Palm of the left hand is toward you. (SEE SKETCH 6)
HOLD ARMS AWAY FROM THE BODY IN A NATURAL, RELAXED POSITION.

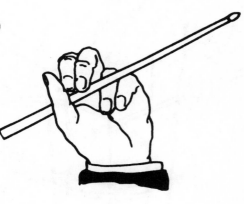

(6)

Playing Position

Posture

You should be able to play in either a standing or sitting position. For the beginner, the standing position is more desirable as it permits a more free movement of the hands, wrists, and arms.

Position of Drum or Pad

The drum or pad should be at such a height as to allow for full-arm strokes. If the drum is too high your arms will be in an unnatural position and become tired. The height of the drum stand should be adjusted to fit the height of the player. The drum should be tilted to about a 45 degree angle to the right. (SEE SKETCH 7)

(7)

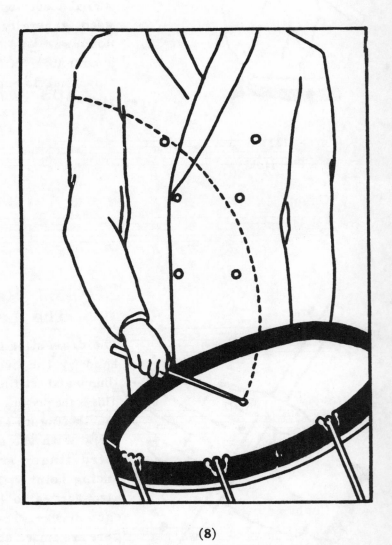

(8)

The TAP and STROKE are the two fundamental stickings. The TAP is a light, soft, unaccented beat and is played with a wrist and finger action. A slight turning motion of the wrist and forearm will produce the desired effect. The head, bead, or button of the drum stick should not be raised more than six or eight inches from the pad or drum head. A feeling of throwing water off the fingers is the action of the wrist and hand. A short quick throwing of the wrist. The secret of good drumming is in the wrist action.

The STROKE is a louder and accented beat and is played the same as the TAP except that the muscles of the forearm are used to strengthen the attack. Throw the water off the fingers a little harder. The heads of the sticks are raised about double the distance (12 to 16 inches) as used for the TAP, and the turning motion of the wrist and forearms is slightly increased. The hands, however, remain in approximately the same relative position to the pad or drum head. THE ARMS MUST NOT MOVE UP AND DOWN. The bead of the sticks make a quarter circle for the TAP and a semi-circle for the STROKE.(SEE SKETCH 8)

OBJECTIVES: (1) Point of playing on pad or drum head.
(2) Relaxing of fingers, wrists, and arms.
(3) Learning how to execute the TAP and STROKE.
(4) Learning to COUNT crotchets.

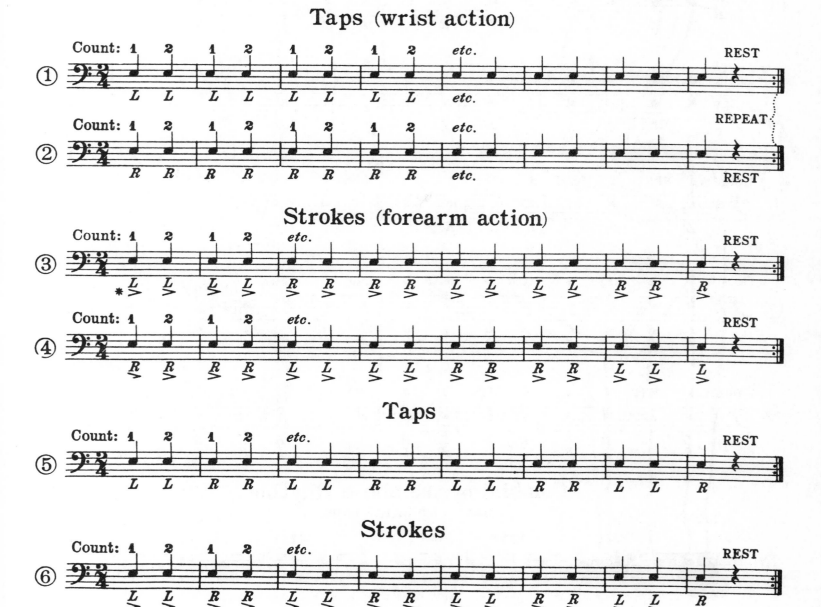

Taps (wrist action)

Strokes (forearm action)

Taps

Strokes

* This sign (>) means to accent, play stronger, louder, more snap.

OBJECTIVES: Playing crotchets with alternate hands.
Playing and counting crotchet rests in $\frac{2}{4}$ time.

Combining the above Rhythms
(Start with either hand)

OBJECTIVE: Playing and counting quavers and quaver rests in $\frac{2}{4}$ time.

Combining the above Rhythms
(Start with either hand)

Songs for Drums and Piano

Alternating strokes
(Start with either hand)

*Merrily

**French Folk Song

***Jingle Bells

*'A TUNE A DAY' For Clarinet, page 3. ** In Clarinet Book, page 4.
*** In Clarinet Book, pages 6 and 30. In Trumpet Book, page 7.

Alla Breve or $\frac{2}{2}$ Time, "Cut Time"

Alla Breve, or cut time ¢ is played the same as $\frac{2}{4}$ time. Each note having half the value as in $\frac{4}{4}$ time, a minim being the unit of a beat.

Semiquavers

A semiquaver 𝄢 is equal to half the value of a quaver 𝄢 Two semiquavers equal one quaver ♫ = ♪, and four semiquavers equal one crotchet ♬ = ♩ Abbreviations for semiquavers ♪ = ♫, ♪ = ♬

Comparison of Alla Breve Time and $\frac{2}{4}$ Time

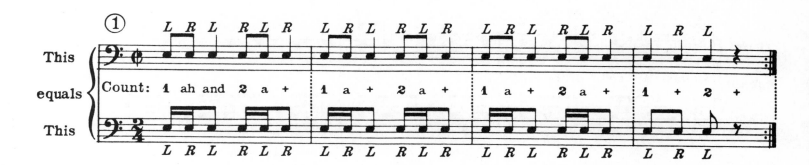

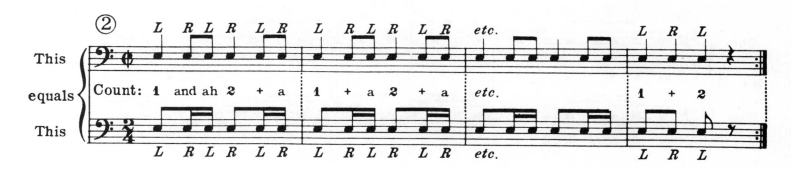

Continuation of Alla Breve and $\frac{2}{4}$ Time

Test Sheet

Review of stickings and rhythms thus far studied. Start with either hand.

In Alla Breve Time

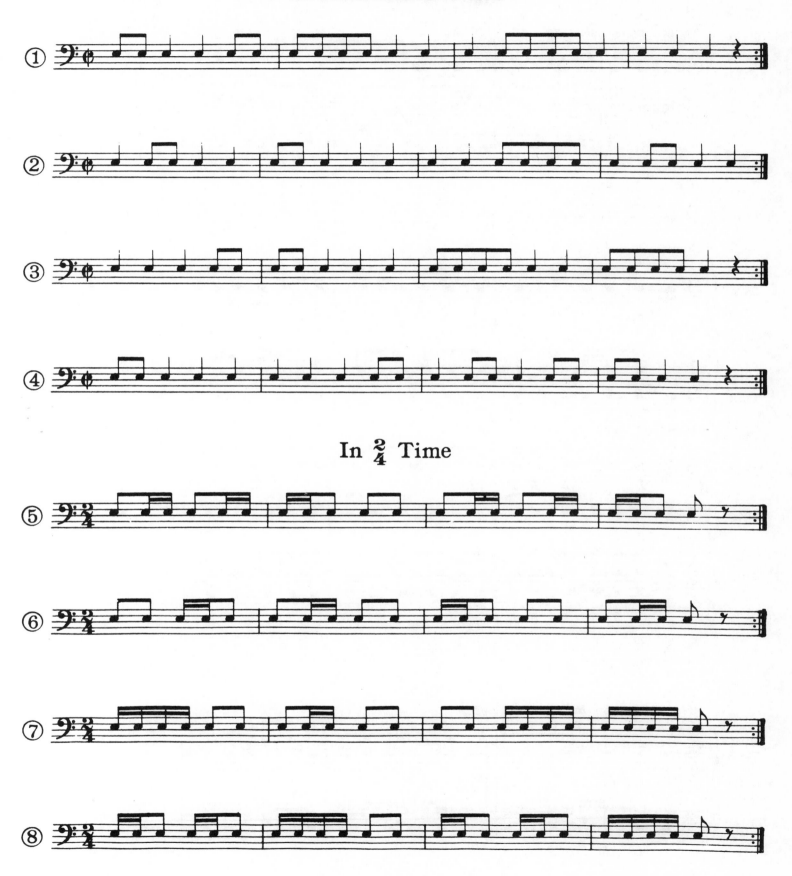

In $\frac{2}{4}$ Time

Three-Four Time

Three-four time ($\frac{3}{4}$) means three crotchets or the equivalent in each bar. Count one to each crotchet; one, two, for each minim and one, two, three for each dotted-minim. The first beat or count is generally played stronger (accented), and the other two beats lighter. Use a stroke for the first count and taps for the other two.

Count Out Loud

Practise exercise one, then two, then one and two without pause. Follow the same plan with each line below.

Comparison of $\frac{3}{8}$ - $\frac{6}{8}$ and Triplets in $\frac{2}{4}$ time

Drums and Piano in Waltz Time

Cielito Lindo

The Bowery

Six-Eight Time

Count six beats to each bar in slow tempo—a quaver (♪) being the unit of a beat.

Count two beats to each bar in fast tempo—a dotted crotchet (♩.) being the unit of a beat.

Preparatory exercise. Repeat each of the following bars until the rhythm of the different groupings is memorized. COUNT ALOUD.

The Flam

The FLAM is one of the most important drum beats and should be practised very diligently. It is actually two notes in one, the "grace note" or tap and the accented stroke. This rudiment (flam) should be practised as follows: Hold the left stick about two inches above the drum or pad, with the right stick held high, about on a level with your shoulder. Strike the drum head with the low left stick, following at once with the right stick. Now hold the right stick low (two inches above the drum) bringing the left stick high (level with your shoulder) and repeat the stroke. When the right hand is high it is called a right hand flam.

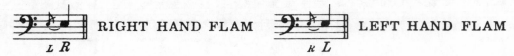

RIGHT HAND FLAM   LEFT HAND FLAM

By combining the two strokes we produce what is called a hand to hand flam. In notation the flam is written with a small grace note played with the low hand, and a large note played with the high hand. The effect of the flam should be like a thick note, the grace note almost becoming part of the heavy stroke, rather than two separate notes.

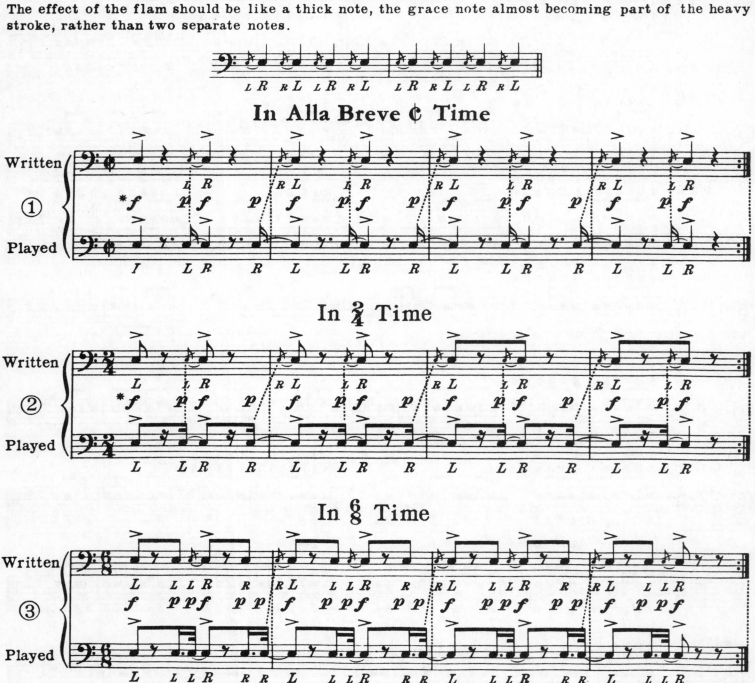

In Alla Breve ¢ Time

In ²⁄₄ Time

In ⁶⁄₈ Time

*f- means loud (FORTE)   p-means soft (PIANO)

Application of the Flam in Various Rhythms
In Alla Breve ¢ Time

As many arrangers do not indicate the flam and other flourishes, the player must use his judgment as to when and where to use them. In the studies below the upper line shows how most drum parts would be written and the lower line shows how an experienced drummer would play them. Use the flam to slightly broaden and accent a note.

* Bass Drum

Marching (Parade) Beats

In 2/4

In 6/8

Five Stroke Roll In 3/4 Time

Four Stroke Ruff

The four stroke ruff is introduced at this time as it is a direct preparation for the seven stroke roll which is taken up in the next lesson. The four stroke ruff consists of three light taps and a stroke. It is written with three grace notes and the principal note. It is generally played from left to right but in a slow tempo may be played from hand to hand. Be sure the three grace notes are played evenly and in the triplet form.

Triplets

Triplets are groups of three notes played in the time of two notes of the same value. They are indicated by a figure 3 and a slur over or under a group of three notes. A triplet of quavers

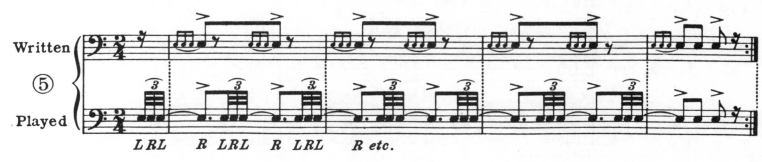

The Seven Stroke Roll

When necessary to sustain a note a little longer than for a five stroke roll we use the seven stroke roll. This seven stroke roll is not played from hand to hand like the five stroke roll but is started with the same hand when a series of successive rolls is called for. Think of the seven stroke roll as four strokes, i. e. (left, right, left, right) or (right, left, right, left) and rebound the first three, the fourth being a single stroke. This roll starts with one hand and finishes with the other. Although this rudiment is generally played from the left hand, a good drummer should be able to start with either hand. By playing the four stroke ruff and rebounding the first three taps the seven stroke roll will be sounded. Practise accenting both the first and last stroke of this roll.

Application of Seven Stroke Roll

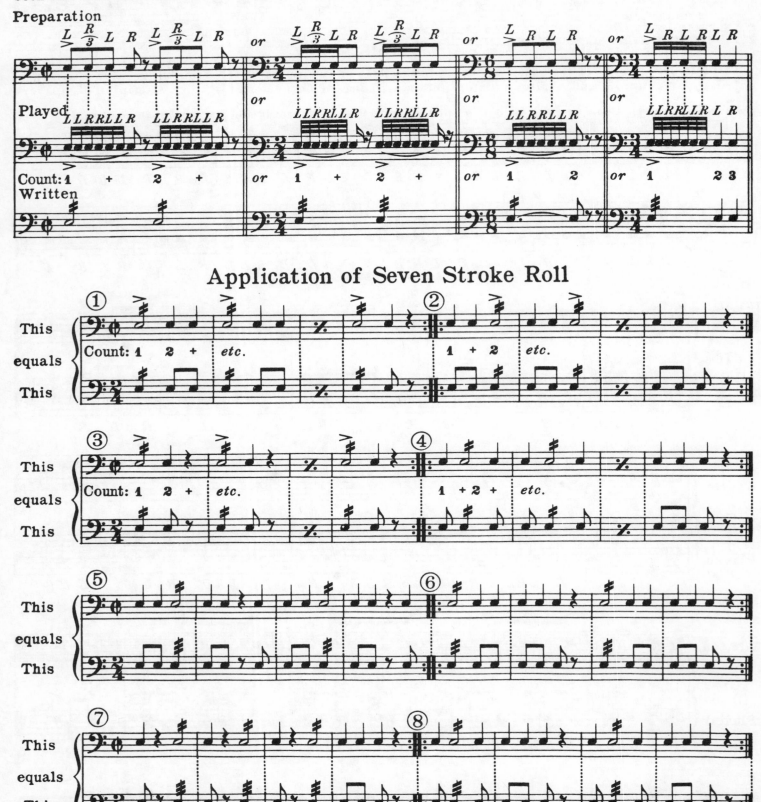